For Chase and Beckett, whose love of
Mr. Met and Home Run Apples inspired
this tale, and for Erica, whose love for all
of us keeps everything else together.

www.mascotbooks.com

We'll Call You Mr. Met!

For more information, please contact:
Mascot Books
560 Herndon Parkway #120
Herndon, VA 20170
info@mascotbooks.com

CPSIA Code: PRT0815A
ISBN-13: 9781620866825

Printed in the United States

WE'LL CALL YOU
MR. MET!™

Written by
John T. Williams

illustrated by
Tim Williams

One summer evening, the mascot babies were playing baseball in their yard when a familiar car drove up. It was their Grandpa and Grandma, who were very excited to see their favorite *Mets* fans.

The mascot babies were excited too, and asked Grandpa to tell their favorite story—how their dad became *Mr. Met*. He was thrilled to share, since it was his favorite story too. The mascot babies gathered round, and the story began…

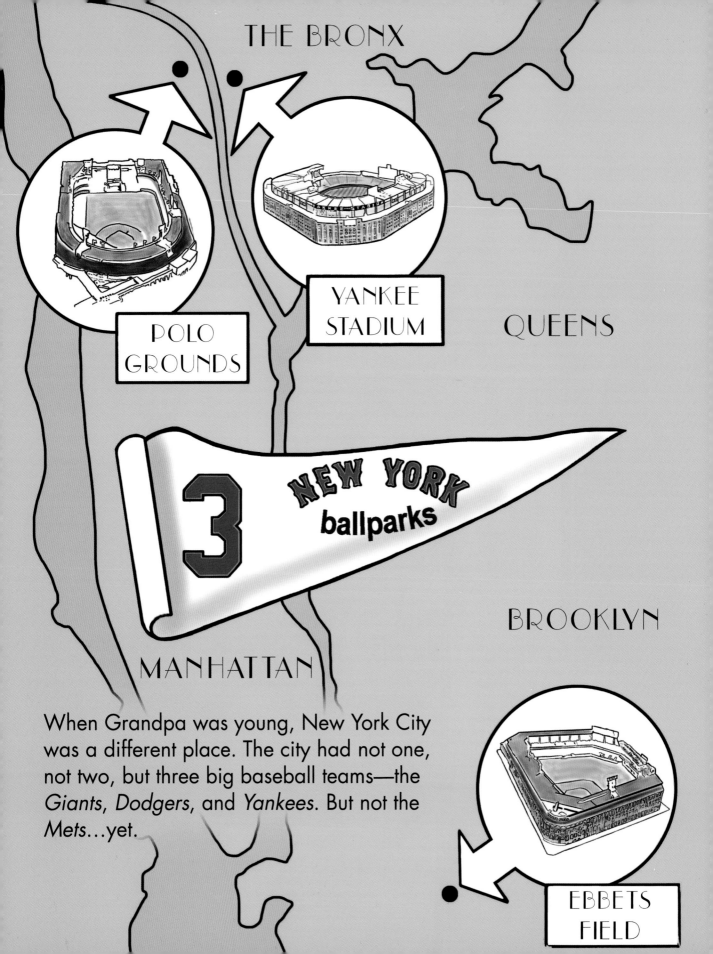

THE BRONX

POLO
GROUNDS

YANKEE
STADIUM

QUEENS

3 NEW YORK ballparks

BROOKLYN

MANHATTAN

When Grandpa was young, New York City was a different place. The city had not one, not two, but three big baseball teams—the *Giants*, *Dodgers*, and *Yankees*. But not the *Mets*…yet.

EBBETS
FIELD

The mascot babies wondered why the *Mets* weren't there long ago. Grandpa reminded them that even though the *Mets* hadn't yet come to play in New York, he could still watch baseball. In fact, he went to games all over the city.

Grandpa grew up in Manhattan, near an old stadium called the *Polo Grounds*. It was shaped like a horseshoe and had dark green seats. He lived so close that he could just walk down a hill to see the *Giants* games.

But that wasn't all he could see—a short walk across a bridge to the Bronx took him to *Yankee Stadium,* and a hop on the subway to Brooklyn took him to see the *Dodgers* play at *Ebbets Field.*

Then, the *Dodgers* and *Giants* decided to move far, far away, to California. New Yorkers tried as hard as they could to keep their teams in town, but it was too late.

Since Grandpa was at all their games, both teams invited him to come along. He said "no thanks"—New York would always be his town.

Every New Yorker wanted a new home team to root for, and one day, their wish came true. A brand new team, the *New York Mets*, would come to play in the city. Everyone was excited!

The new *Mets* didn't win very often at first, but Grandpa and his little boy sat in the bleachers for every game. They watched together as New York fell in love with its *Amazin' Mets*.

One morning, old Casey, the *Mets* manager, saw them sitting way out in the bleachers. He looked at the little boy with the baseball-shaped head, and said, "Hey kid, I've seen you and your dad here for every game. You sure must love the *Amazin' Mets*."

Casey thought for a minute, then said, "Kid, how would you like to be our new mascot? We'll call you *Mr. Met*. You'll be our number one fan." The boy—who grew up to become the mascot babies' dad—smiled, shook Casey's hand, and put on a brand-new *Mets* cap. From then on, he was *Mr. Met*.

The following year, the *Mets* moved into beautiful new *Shea Stadium*—and *Mr. Met* went with them. The team still lost a lot more than it won, but the right players and coaches came along and things started getting better.

Everything came together in 1969, when the *Mets* terrific pitching, clutch hitting, and great manager shocked the world and went from worst to first. The "Miracle Mets" won the *World Series*, and *Mr. Met* celebrated with them!

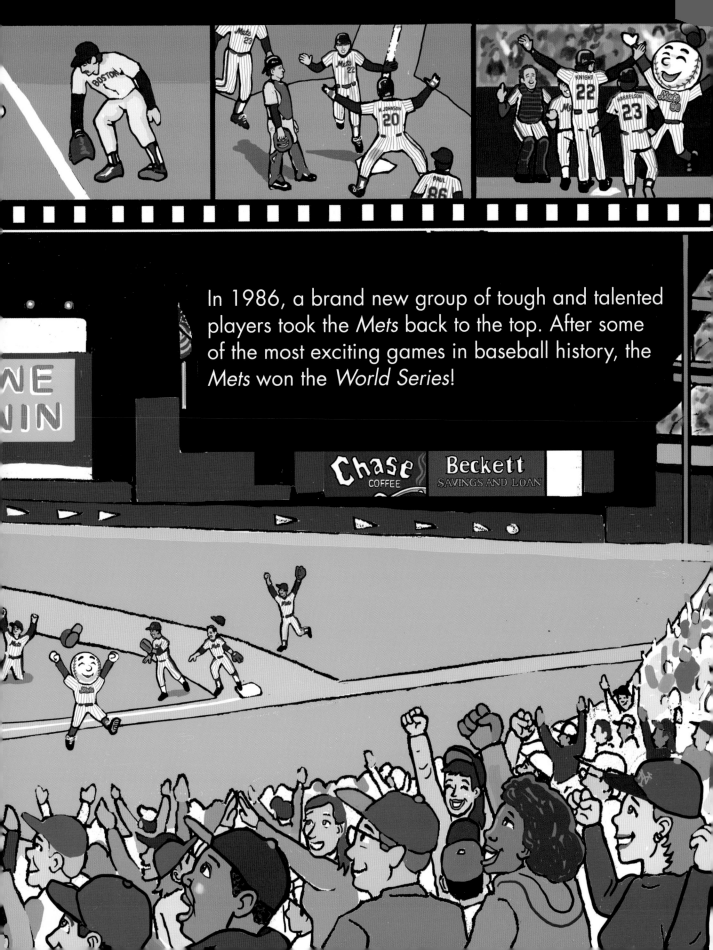

In 1986, a brand new group of tough and talented players took the *Mets* back to the top. After some of the most exciting games in baseball history, the *Mets* won the *World Series*!

Led by *Mr. Met*, it was time for a new era at *Shea*: great defense, strong pitching, and a superstar catcher took the *Mets* to a *subway World Series*. The excitement was back!

Soon after, the *Mets* moved out of *Shea Stadium* and into beautiful *Citi Field*. While many things are different, a lot is still the same—the home run apple, the blue and orange colors, and, of course, *Mr. Met!*

As the sun set behind *Citi Field*, *Mr. Met* joined everyone on the outfield grass. It was a perfect baseball evening—and a great way to celebrate the truly amazing tale of how their whole family got to "Meet the *Mets!*"

Fun Facts About

See if you can spot some of our favorite *Mets* details scattered throughout the book.

1. "Meet the *Mets*" is the team's official fight song, and was introduced in 1962. The song is still in use today, as is the 1984 re-recording that is sometimes played in its place.

2. From 1903-1957, New York had three *MLB* teams, and hosted 13 "subway" *World Series* (7 *Yankees-Dodgers*, 6 *Yankees-Giants*).

3. The *Polo Grounds* was in Upper Manhattan, just across the Harlem River from *Yankee Stadium*, while *Ebbets Field* sat in the heart of Brooklyn.

4. The *Dodgers* and *Giants* moved to California after the 1957 season, making them the first two West Coast teams in *Major League Baseball*.

5. The *Mets* team colors were inspired by New York's two prior *National League* teams (*Dodgers* blue, *Giants* orange) and are two of the three colors on the New York City flag.

6. The *Mets* began play in 1962, and the young expansion team was quickly nicknamed the "*Amazin' Mets*" by legendary manager Casey Stengel.

the *Mets*

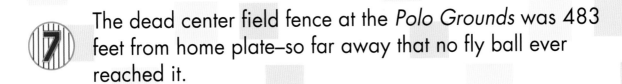

7 The dead center field fence at the *Polo Grounds* was 483 feet from home plate–so far away that no fly ball ever reached it.

8 Named for William Shea, a lawyer who led the charge to bring the *Mets* to New York, *Shea Stadium* was a modern, bright, futuristic facility when it opened in 1964.

9 The 1969 "Miracle Mets" swept the *Atlanta Braves* in the first *National League Championship Series* and stunned the *Baltimore Orioles* in 5 games to win the *World Series*.

10 The 1986 *Mets* dominated the *National League*, winning the *World Series* in one of the most exciting postseasons in baseball history.

11 The 2000 *National League Champion Mets* faced the *New York Yankees* in the city's first *Subway Series* since 1956. After 45 exciting years, the *Mets* left *Shea Stadium* after the 2008 season.

12 Many *Citi Field* features were inspired by New York's *National League* past: the Home Run Apple and orange foul poles (*Shea Stadium*), green seats (*Polo Grounds*), and Jackie Robinson Rotunda (*Ebbets Field*).

About the Author

Born and raised in the Bronx, John T. Williams spent many summer days at sunny *Shea Stadium* with his very patient mother. A lifelong New Yorker and dedicated *Mets* fan, he and his family live in Manhattan.